SCHOOLS LIBRARY
AND INFORMATION SERVICE

KU-424-843

Schools Library and Information Services

S00000685051

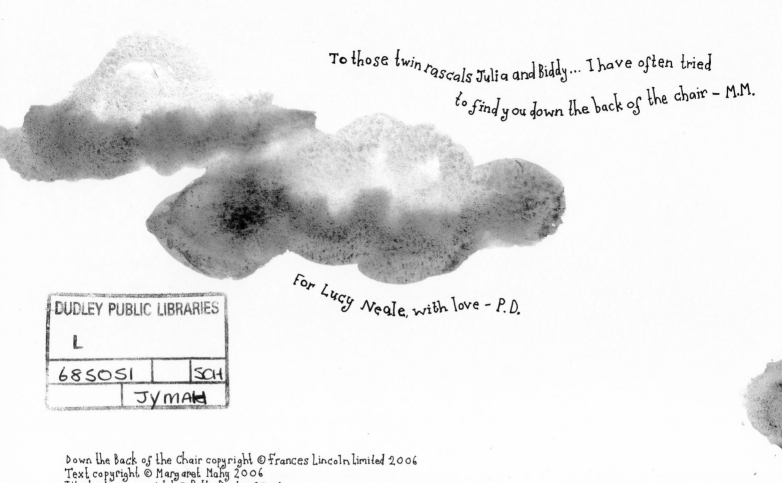

To those twin rascals Julia and Biddy... I have often tried
to find you down the back of the chair – M.M.

For Lucy Neale, with love – P.D.

DUDLEY PUBLIC LIBRARIES

L

685051 | | SCH

JYMAH

Down the Back of the Chair copyright © Frances Lincoln Limited 2006
Text copyright © Margaret Mahy 2006
Illustration copyright © Polly Dunbar 2006

The right of Margaret Mahy to be identified as the Author
and Polly Dunbar to be identified as the Illustrator of this work
has been asserted by them in accordance with the Copyright,
Designs and Patents Act, 1988.

First published in Great Britain in 2006 by Frances Lincoln Children's Books,
4 Torriano Mews, Torriano Avenue, London NW5 2RZ

www.franceslincoln.com

All rights reserved.
No part of this publication may be reproduced, stored in a retrieval system,
or transmitted, in any form, or by any means, electrical, mechanical,
photocopying, recording or otherwise without the prior written permission
of the publisher or a licence permitting restricted copying. In the United
Kingdom such licences are issued by the Copyright Licensing Agency.
90 Tottenham Court Road, London W1P 9HE.

British Library Cataloguing in Publication Data available on request.

ISBN 1845074408

Printed in China
9 8 7 6 5 4 3 2 1

Down the Back of the Chair

Margaret Mahy

Illustrated by Polly Dunbar

FRANCES

LINCOLN

CHILDREN'S

BOOKS

Our car is slow to start and go.
We can't afford a new one.
Now, if you please, Dad's lost the keys.
We're facing rack and ruin.

No car, no work! No work, no pay!
We're growing poorer day by day.
No wonder Dad is turning grey.
The morning is a blue one.

Nothing but dockets
in his pockets,
raging with despair,

Dad acts appalled!
Though nearly bald,
he tries to tear his hair.

But Mary,
who is barely two,
says, "Dad should do
what I would do!

I lose a lot, but I find a few —
down the back of the chair."

He's patted himself and searched the shelf.
He's hunted here and there,
so now he'll kneel and try to feel
right down the back of the chair.

Oh, it seemed to grin as his hand went in.
He felt tingling under his skin.
What will a troubled father win
from down the back of the chair?

Some hairy string and a diamond ring

were down the back of the chair.

Pineapple peel and a conger eel

were down the back of the chair.

A sip, a sup, a sop, a song, a spider seven inches long.

No wonder that it smells so strong – down the back of the chair.

A packet of pins
and **one** of the twins,

down the back of the chair.

A pan, a fan that belonged to Gran,

down the back of the chair...

A crumb,

a comb,

a clown,

a cap,

a pirate with a treasure map,

a dragon trying to take a nap –

down the back

of the chair.

A cake, a drake, a smiling snake,

down the back of the chair.

A string of pearls,
a lion with curls,
down the back
of the chair.

A skink, a skunk, a skate, a ski,

a couple of elephants

drinking tea,

a bandicoot and a bumblebee, down the back of the chair.

But what is this?
Oh, bliss! Oh, bliss!

Down the back of the chair.

The long lost will

of Uncle Bill,

down the back

of the chair.

His money box all crammed with cash,
tangled up in a scarlet sash.
There's pleasure, treasure, toys and trash –
down the back of the chair.

"I've found my dreams,"

our father beams,

"down the back of the chair.

At last I see

how life can be,

down the back

of the chair."

"Forget the keys! We're poor no more.
Just call a taxi to the door."

A taxi shot out with a roar

from down the back of the chair.

The chair
   the chair,
      the challenging chair,
         the champion chair, the cheerful chair,
   the charming chair, the children's chair,
         the chopped and chipped, but chosen chair.
   To think our fortune
                  waited there –
            down the back
                  of the
               chair!